Usborne
Royal
colouring book

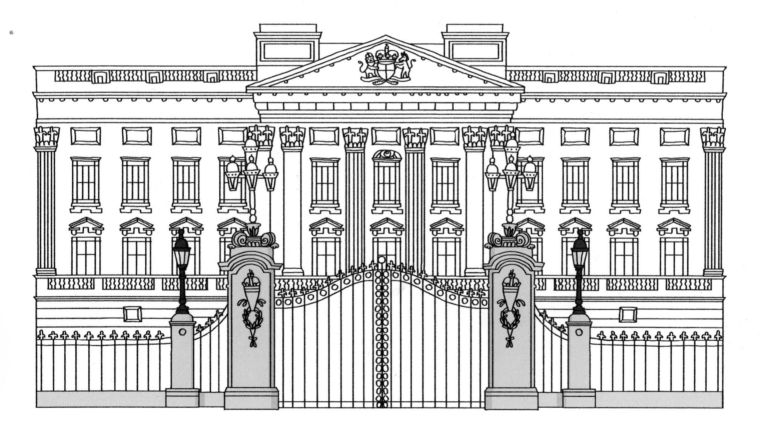

Illustrated by Sophie Crichton

Written by Struan Reid

Designed by Jamie Jonathan Ball

and Ian McNee

The Bayeux Tapestry

In 1066, Duke William of Normandy defeated King Harold of England at the Battle of Hastings and crowned himself William I – better known as William the Conqueror. The Bayeux Tapestry records the story of the battle.

HIC WILLELM:DVX   VL:ANGLI

It isn't really a tapestry at all, but a very long piece of linen cloth with scenes that tell the story embroidered in coloured wools. Although it was made more than 900 years ago, the colours are still very bright and fresh.

ET FRANCI:

The Tower of London

The Tower of London is a royal palace, built by William the Conqueror soon after he invaded England. Yeoman Warders act as guards, and the oldest part is known as the White Tower.

Yeoman Warders, or 'Beefeaters', dress in red and gold uniforms.

The White Tower is actually grey and white.

Black ravens live in the grounds.

Henry VIII and his six wives

Henry VIII, one of the most famous kings of England, reigned from 1509 until 1547. He was extremely powerful and loved dressing up in magnificent clothes, with fur cloaks, feather hats and gold chains.

Henry VIII

Anne of Cleves, fourth wife

Jane Seymour,
third wife

Catherine of Aragon,
first wife

Anne Boleyn,
second wife

Catherine Parr,
sixth wife

Catherine Howard,
fifth wife

Henry was married six times. He divorced his first wife and executed the second. His third wife died and he divorced the fourth. He executed his fifth wife, and his sixth wife managed to outlive him.

Hampton Court

Hampton Court was a favourite palace of Queen Elizabeth I, Henry VIII's daughter. It lies to the west of London, beside the River Thames.

Here the Queen is being carried on a litter, attended by her
courtiers and ladies-in-waiting. You can see the walls of the palace
behind her. They are built of pink-red brick and white stone.

Royal costumes

These costumes were worn during the time of the Tudors, who ruled from 1485 until 1603. They are made from furs and embroidered silks and velvets.

King Henry VII wears a red and gold cloak trimmed with ermine fur.

His wife, Elizabeth of York, is wearing a dress of gold, red and blue.

Royal costumes were designed to be as colourful as possible, so that they shone and glittered as the king and queen walked along. The clothes were finished with gold chains and long necklaces studded with precious stones.

Anne Boleyn, second wife of King Henry VIII

Queen Elizabeth I, daughter of Henry VIII and Anne Boleyn

More royal costumes

These clothes were worn by kings and queens in the 17th, 18th and 19th centuries. King Charles I (reigned 1625-49) was a member of the Scottish Stuart family. The Stuarts ruled England and Scotland from 1603 until 1714.

Here he's wearing a blue jacket with lace collar.

Henrietta Maria, Charles I's wife, is wearing a gold dress with silver collar.

The last Stuart monarch was Queen Anne, who died in 1714. After the Stuarts came the Hanoverians, who were descended from Charles I's sister Elizabeth. They originally came from Hanover in Germany.

King George IV (1820-30) wears silver clothes under a blue cloak and red sashes.

Queen Anne (1702-14)

Fireworks on the Thames

In 1749, during the reign of King George II, there was a spectacular fireworks display on the River Thames in London. It was held to celebrate the end of a war. An orchestra played music as the fireworks lit up the night sky.

The Crown Jewels

The Crown Jewels are some of the most valuable jewels in the world. They're used at the coronation of every king or queen. Here are some of the main ones.

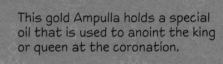

This Orb is a golden sphere with a band of precious stones around the middle.

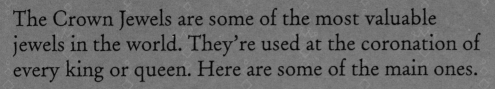

This sceptre contains the second largest diamond in the world.

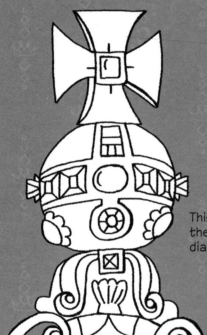

This gold Ampulla holds a special oil that is used to anoint the king or queen at the coronation.

Saint Edward's Crown is used to crown the king or queen. It is made of solid gold and precious stones, lined with purple velvet.

Royal symbols

The coat of arms of Queen Elizabeth II consists of the symbols that represent the three different kingdoms that make up the United Kingdom – England, Scotland and Northern Ireland. Wales is a principality.

Royal coat of arms of the United Kingdom of Great Britain and Northern Ireland

Red lion for Scotland, with three gold lions for England below

Three gold lions for England

Golden harp for Northern Ireland

DIEU ET MON DROIT

IN DEFENS

The royal crest of Scotland has a red lion on top of a golden crown.

Red dragon of Wales

This is the Royal Standard, or personal flag, of the Queen.

Queen Victoria's Christmas

The year is 1850, and Queen Victoria is celebrating Christmas at Windsor Castle with her husband, Prince Albert, and five of their nine children.

The Queen is wearing a pale blue and gold dress, with a jewelled tiara on her head.

Prince Albert wears a dark blue coat, white shirt and black breeches and stockings.

The Christmas tree is decorated with candles and colourful bows and baubles.

Elizabeth II's coronation

It's 1953, and Elizabeth II is arriving at Westminster Abbey where she will be crowned Queen. She has travelled from Buckingham Palace in a golden coach pulled by white horses. The Queen is wearing a white and silver dress and lots of diamonds.

This is a Yeoman of the Guard, a personal bodyguard to the Queen. His uniform is red, gold and black.

Gold coach with red interior

The coachman wears a black hat, red and gold jacket, white trousers and black boots.

Royal carriages and barges

Riders in red, gold and white uniforms with black hats

White flags with blue and red crosses

Black carriage with golden roof and lamps

On ceremonial occasions, such as the opening of Parliament, the Queen travels in a carriage pulled by horses. This golden river barge was specially made for her Diamond Jubilee.

Trooping the Colour

Trooping the Colour is a ceremony performed in front of the Queen by regiments of the British and Commonwealth armies. Also known as the Queen's Birthday Parade, it is held every June on her official birthday.

Members of the army band
wear red and black uniforms,
with black furry hats.

The royal wedding

In the spring of 2011, Prince William of Wales, grandson of Queen Elizabeth II, married Catherine Middleton at Westminster Abbey in London. Thousands of well-wishers watched as they drove past.

Royal palaces

Over the centuries, Britain's kings and queens have built palaces and castles all over the country. Some of them are still in use, while others have been demolished or turned into museums.

One of the largest royal palaces is Hampton Court. Henry VIII was the first king to live there and King George II was the last. Today, you can visit the royal apartments and see the beautiful gardens, including a famous maze.

Kew Palace, to the west of London, is a small pink brick palace. King George III lived there with his family.

You can visit the palace inside Kew Gardens.

The Palace of Holyroodhouse in Edinburgh is the Queen's official residence in Scotland.

When the Queen isn't staying, you can look around the magnificent rooms.

Henry VIII's Crown

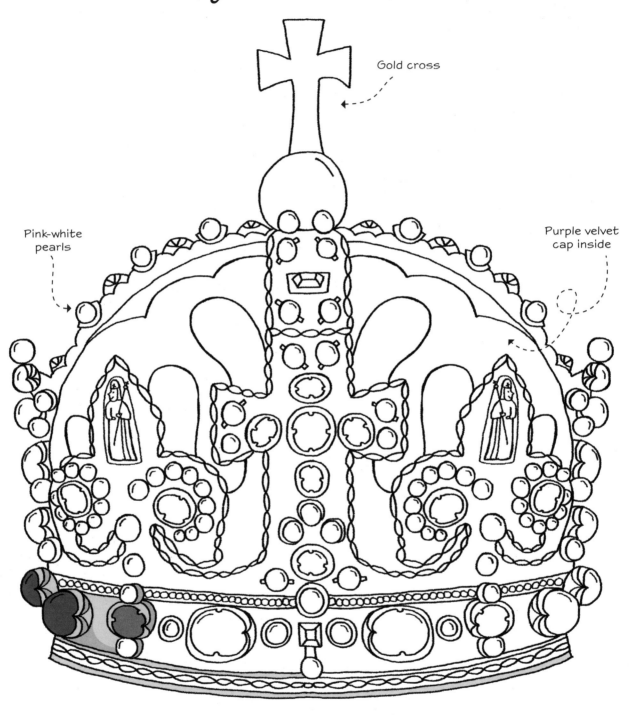

Gold cross

Pink-white pearls

Purple velvet cap inside

This is a copy of a crown made of gold and covered in jewels once worn by King Henry VIII. The original was destroyed more than 350 years ago.